really easy keyboard

C000170720

CHART HITS

Published by
Wise Publications
14-15 Berners Street,
London W1T 3LJ, UK.

Exclusive Distributors:
Music Sales Limited
Distribution Centre, Newmarket Road,
Bury St Edmunds, Suffolk IP33 3YB, UK.
Music Sales Pty Limited
Level 4, Lisgar House,
30-32 Carrington Street,
Sydney, NSW 2000 Australia.

Order No. AM1011978
ISBN 978-1-78558-328-5

Music processed by Sarah Lofthouse, SEL Music Art Ltd.
Music arranged by Fiona Bolton.
Edited by Louise Unsworth.

Printed in the EU.

www.musicsales.com

really easy keyboard

#1 Spring/Summer 2017

CHART HITS

Wise Publications
part of The Music Sales Group
London/New York/Paris/Sydney/Copenhagen/Berlin/Madrid/Hong Kong/Tokyo

CONTENTS

Keyboard introduction 6

24K Magic Bruno Mars 10

Ain't My Fault Zara Larsson 12

Bad Things Machine Gun Kelly & Camila Cabello 9

By Your Side Jonas Blue feat. RAYE 14

Castle On The Hill Ed Sheeran 16

Closer The Chainsmokers feat. Halsey 18

Human Rag'n'Bone Man 20

I Would Like Zara Larsson 22

Let Me Love You DJ Snake feat. Justin Bieber 24

No Lie Sean Paul feat. Dua Lipa 26

Not In Love M.O feat. Kent Jones 28

Now And Later Sage The Gemini 30

On Hold The xx 34

Rockabye Clean Bandit feat. Sean Paul & Anne-Marie 36

September Song JP Cooper 38

Shape Of You Ed Sheeran 40

So Good Louisa Johnson 42

Starboy The Weeknd feat. Daft Punk 44

We Don't Talk Anymore Charlie Puth feat. Selena Gomez 31

You Don't Know Me Jax Jones feat. RAYE 46

You Want Me Tom Zanetti feat. Sadie Ama 48

YOUR KEYBOARD

Although keyboards vary from make to make and model to model, they all have the same basic features:

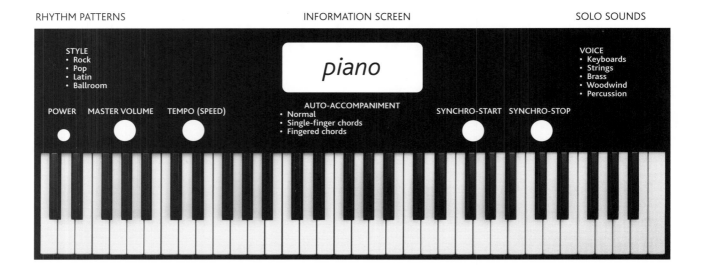

Power (mains)

This turns the keyboard on or off. Most keyboards can run on batteries or from the mains, using a suitable transformer, which is usually supplied with your keyboard.

Master Volume

This controls the overall 'loudness' of the instrument. It is either in the form of a slider, button or knob, which can be set anywhere from minimum to maximum.

Auto-accompaniment

This feature adds an automatic accompaniment to your melody, which you can use in various different ways.

Tempo (Speed)

This controls the speed of the accompaniment rhythm. It can be set anywhere from minimum to maximum, or may display an exact tempo, e.g. ♩ =112. The number displayed is the number of beats per minute, and varies between about 45 to about 220.

Synchro-start

This button activates the auto-accompaniment and synchronises it to when you start playing.

Rhythm or Style

This feature adds a drum rhythm to your melody. You can choose between a number of different styles, e.g. rock, pop, Latin, swing etc.

Voices or Solo Sounds

These might be grouped in different 'types' of voice, e.g. strings, woodwind, or they may be grouped by instrument, depending on how many different voices your particular keyboard offers. They add colour and interest to your melodies.

Information Screen

Most modern keyboards incorporate a digital screen which provides information about which settings you are using, e.g: which voice and rhythm you have selected, and whether you are using auto-accompaniment.

Voice settings

The voices (solo sounds) on your keyboard might be divided into general categories, such as keyboards, woodwind, brass, strings, and so on (a bit like an orchestra). If, for example, you want to use a piano sound, go into keyboards, press 01 on the number pad (01 is an almost universal number set up for a basic piano sound) and the piano sound will appear on the screen.

Rhythm settings

There will be many different rhythm patterns (sometimes called styles) available on your keyboard. Like voices, rhythms will probably be subdivided into categories. Typical rhythm categories are rock, pop, ballroom and Latin.

In your rock category, select one of the rock variations, for example 'rock pop', and press start. Listen to this rhythm pattern for a few moments, then try speeding it up or slowing it down using your tempo control. Try other rock variations, or totally different rhythms, such as quickstep (probably in the ballroom category) or bossa nova (probably in the Latin category).

Now, instead of the start button, select synchro, or synchro-start. Play any note in the lower register (the lower half of the keyboard) and the rhythm section will start automatically. Press synchro again and the rhythm will stop.

See your owner's manual for specific details.

READING NOTATION

To perform the songs in this book, you will need to play the chords with your left hand and the melody with your right. The chords you need to play are written above the notation and the shapes for these chords are shown at the beginning of each song.

Before you start to play, make sure you have the correct voice, rhythm and tempo settings.

Here are some helpful reference notes for reading the notation:

Notes values and rests

The note value tells you the duration of a note—how many beats it lasts. When read in sequence, note values show the rhythm of the music.

Each has its own rest, which indicates a silence for the equivalent duration.

symbol	name	duration	rest
𝅝	semibreve	4 beats	▬
𝅗𝅥 or	minim	2 beats	▬
𝅘𝅥 or	crotchet	1 beat	𝄽
𝅘𝅥𝅮 or	quaver	½ beat	𝄾
𝅘𝅥𝅯 or	semiquaver	¼ beat	𝄿

Sharps, flats and naturals

♯ A **sharp** sign raises the pitch of a note by a semitone to the very next key on the right.

♭ A **flat** sign lowers the pitch of a note by a semitone to the very next key on the left.

♮ A **natural** sign cancels the effect of a sharp or a flat, representing the unaltered pitch.

A **key signature** is written at the start of each line of music. It tells us which notes should be played as *sharps* or *flats* and saves writing a ♯ or ♭ sign every time these notes appear.

Time signatures

The **time signature** appears after the key signature at the beginning of the music.

The *upper figure* shows the number of beats in each bar and the *lower figure* tells us what note duration gets one beat.

$\frac{4}{4}$ or **C** = four crotchet beats per bar
(also called common time)

$\frac{3}{4}$ = three crotchet beats per bar

$\frac{2}{4}$ = two crotchet beats per bar

$\frac{2}{2}$ or **¢** = two minim beats per bar
(also called cut common time)

$\frac{6}{8}$ = six quaver beats per bar

$\frac{12}{8}$ = twelve quaver beats per bar

Repeat signs and other navigation marks

‖: This is an end **repeat sign**, which tells you to repeat back from the beginning, or from the start repeat: :‖

⌐1.⌐ ⌐2.⌐ **First-** and **second-time bars** are used to indicate passages in a repeated section that are only performed on certain playings.

D.C. *(Da Capo)* tells you to repeat from the beginning.

D.C. al Fine *(Da Capo al Fine)* tells you to repeat from the beginning to the end, or up to **Fine** .

D.S. *(Dal Segno)* tells you to repeat from the sign 𝄋 .

D.S. al Coda *(Dal Segno al Coda)* tells you to repeat from the sign 𝄋 and then, when you reach **to Coda** ⊕, you should jump to the Coda, marked ⊕ **Coda** .

NOTE GUIDE

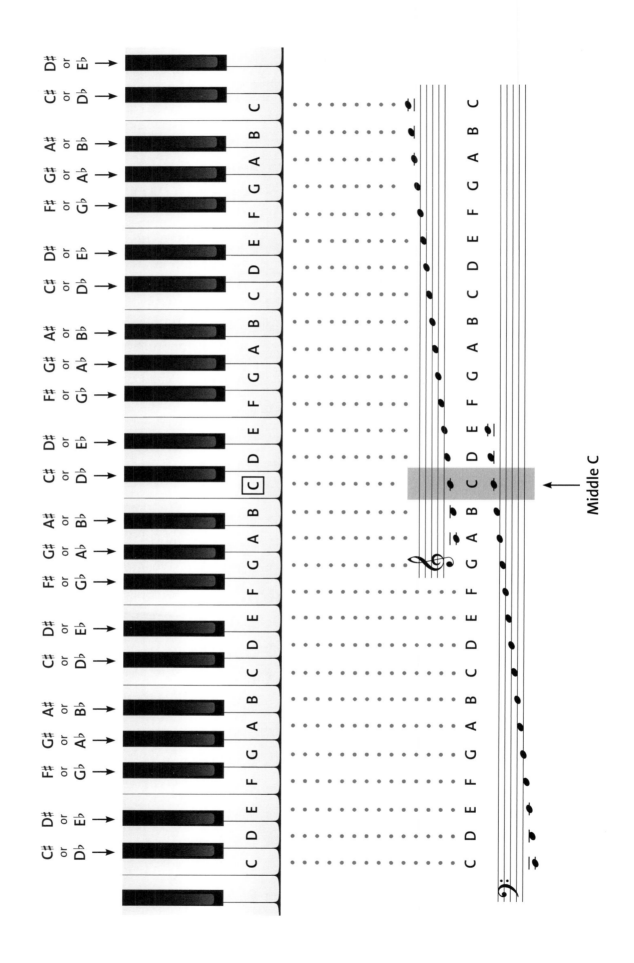

Middle C

Bad Things

Words & Music by Richard Baker, Madison Love, Anthony Scalzo,
Karla Cabello, Alex Schwartz & Joe Khajadourian

'Bad Things' is a song about the relationship between a 'good girl' and a 'bad boy', played by Camila Cabello of Fifth Harmony girl group fame, and rapper, Machine Gun Kelly. In order to record the track, the duo had to collaborate longdistance over the phone and FaceTime. It took over 100 takes before the pair were finally happy with Cabello's vocal line!

Hints & Tips: Position your hand and fingers carefully before the start of each melodic phrase to help achieve a *legato* feel. Remember, this song is in 2. Take note of the slow tempo when placing the quavers in the right hand.

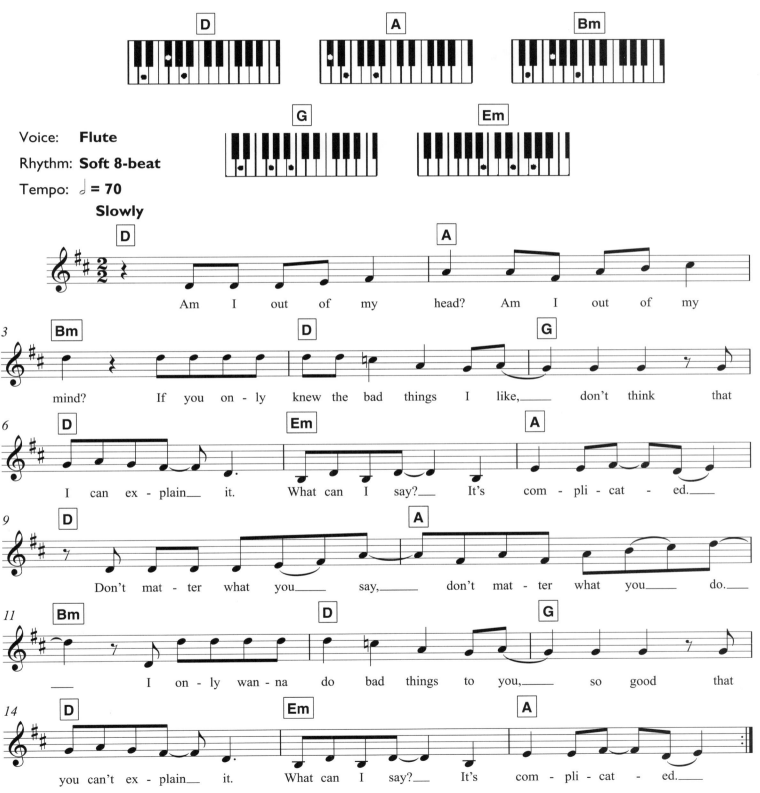

24K Magic

Words & Music by Philip Lawrence, Peter Hernandez & Christopher "Brody" Brown

The first single of his third studio album of the same title, Mars calls this song 'an invitation to the party'. The fun, celebratory vibe of the track echoes his previous smash hit, 'Uptown Funk', which was storming the charts at No. 1 while '24K Magic' was in the making. The track affirms that Mars's party atmosphere is of the highest quality with the reference to 24-karat gold—the purest of them all!

Hints & Tips: A lot of the notes have an 'x' instead of a regular notehead, showing that the lyrics are spoken—why not try creating a melody by choosing pitches for these notes?

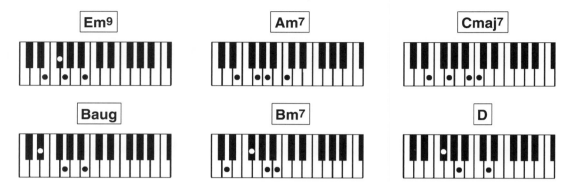

Voice: **Tenor Sax**

Rhythm: **Dance Funk**

Tempo: ♩ = 104

Funky

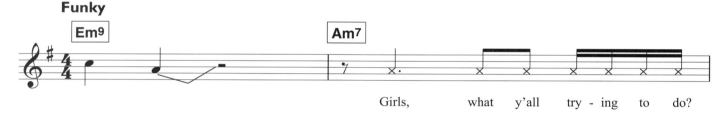

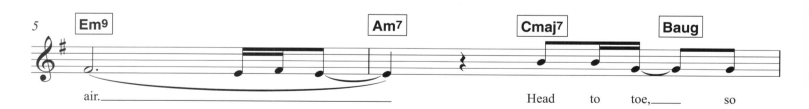

I'm a dan - ger - ous man___ with some mon - ey in my poc - ket. Keep up!

So ma - ny pret - ty girls a - round me and they're wak - ing up the rock - et. Keep up!

Why you mad? Fix your face, ain't my fault that y'all be jock - in'. Keep up!

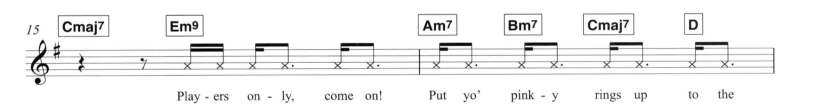

Play - ers on - ly, come on! Put yo' pink - y rings up to the

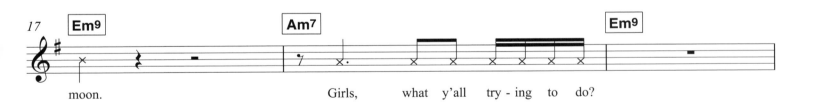

moon.   Girls, what y'all try - ing to do?

Twen - ty - four ka - rat ma - gic in the air.___

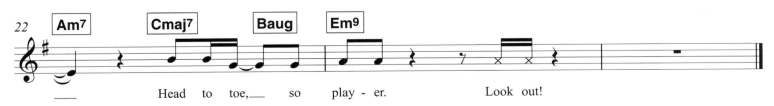

___ Head to toe,___ so play - er.   Look out!

Ain't My Fault

Words & Music by Uzoechi Emenike, Zara Larsson & Mack

After winning Talang, a Swedish talent show, at the age of 10, Zara Larsson was destined for a career in music.
Still only in her late teens when the single was released, 'Ain't My Fault' describes Larsson's attraction to a
good-looking man and her subsequent actions, for which she thinks she shouldn't be made responsible.
Initially, it was written about two women arguing over a man, but Zara appealed to the 'girl code'—that
girls should stick together—and decided not to record the original lyrics.

Hints & Tips: The melody line in this song has lots of off-beat rhythms.
Use the first quaver of bars 1, 3, 5 & 7 to 'bounce' onto the syncopated crotchet.

Bm	G	F#m	F#
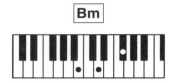		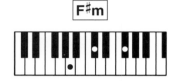	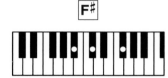

Voice: **Electric Guitar**

Rhythm: **Fusion**

Tempo: = 130

Strong

It ain't my fault you keep turn-ing me on. It ain't my fault you got,

got me so gone. It ain't my fault I'm not leav-ing a - lone. It

ain't my fault you keep turn - ing me on. I can't talk right now, I like what I'm

see - ing, feel - ing shocked right now. Could - a stopped right now, got - ta get it,

get it while it's hot right now. Oh my God, what is this?

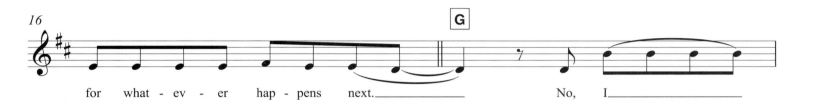

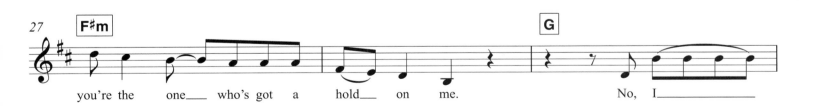

13

By Your Side

Words & Music by George Astasio, Jason Pebworth, Jonathan Shave, Guy Robin & Grace Barker

Jonas Blue's first single was a house music cover of Tracy Chapman's 'Fast Car', which shot him to fame in 2016. 'By Your Side' is another club classic and the third single from the electronic dance producer. Teenage singing sensation RAYE features on the track and has worked with a number of other contemporary names, including Charlie XCX and the songwriter/producer Jax Jones, whose song featuring RAYE also appears in this book.

Hints & Tips: The melody for this song uses mostly white notes, but watch out for the B♭s that crop up on the second page! It may help to mark these in with a pencil to remind you.

Voice: **Oboe**

Rhythm: **House**

Tempo: ♩ = 120

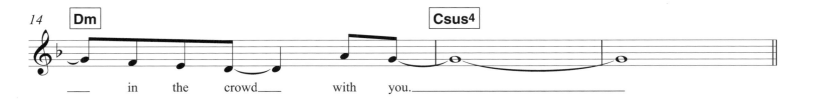

in the crowd____ with you._____

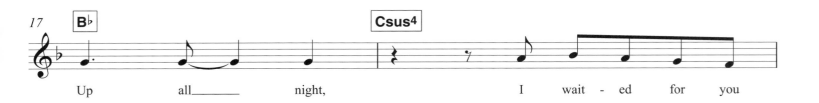

Up all_____ night, I wait - ed for you

all my_____ life. Hold my hand and keep me close, I'll nev - er let you

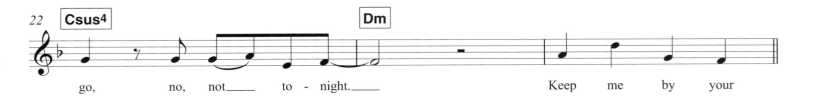

go, no, not____ to - night.____ Keep me by your

side. By,____ by your side. By,____ by your side. By,____ by your

side. Your, your, your, your, your, your side. By,____ by your side. By,____ by your

side. By,____ by... Keep me by your side.____

Castle On The Hill

Words & Music by Benjamin Levin & Ed Sheeran

Famous for his down-to-earth attitude to being a celebrity, Sheeran wrote this song about his home town of Framlingham in Suffolk, saying, 'This is a love song for Suffolk, because I don't think anyone has ever done that'. The video for the song was shot in Framlingham and even stars an Ed Sheeran lookalike, who is actually a young student at Thomas Mills High School, where Sheeran used to study!

Hints & Tips: Play the melody in a 'speakerly' fashion—keep it relaxed.
Try not to rush the syncopated rhythms in the bridge (from bar 17).

Voice: **Bass Clarinet**

Rhythm: **Country Rock**

Tempo: ♩ = 130

Closer

Words & Music by Joseph King, Isaac Slade, Shaun Frank, Ashley Frangipane, Andrew Taggart & Frederic Kennett

Keeping it stateside, American DJ duo The Chainsmokers got together with American singer-songwriter Halsey to record 'Closer'. Listeners are treated to the first vocal performance from The Chainsmokers' Drew Taggart as he sings with Halsey in a romantic comedy-style duet. The duo cite pop-punk band Blink 182 as one of their biggest influences for the track, particularly their song 'I Miss You', which they played on repeat!

Hints & Tips: Shape the repetitive phrases from bar 17 onwards using *crescendos* and *diminuendos*, and experiment with placing a slight emphasis on certain syllables.

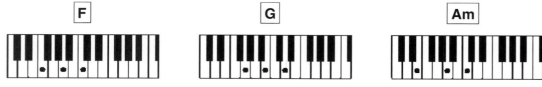

Voice: **Electric Piano**

Rhythm: **Indy Dance**

Tempo: ♩ = 96

Human

Words & Music by Jamie Hartman & Rory Graham

Rag'n'Bone Man is deeply influenced by blues and hip-hop music, and this inspiration infiltrates into his own sound, as you can hear in 'Human'. His first taste of performing in public came when his father persuaded him to sing at a local blues jam at the age of 19, after which he was booked for local gigs and felt encouraged to work on his own projects. The stage name Rag'n'Bone Man was a result of his appreciation of *Steptoe & Son*, a British TV sitcom about a father and son's 'rag-and-bone' business.

Hints & Tips: Prepare your right hand for the melody in this piece by practising scales and arpeggios in the key of B minor.

Voice: **Brass Ensemble**

Rhythm: **Soul Rock**

Tempo: ♩ = 150

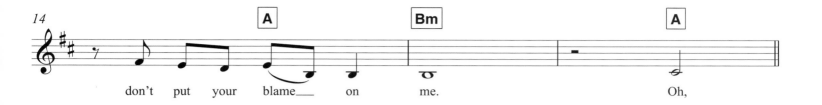

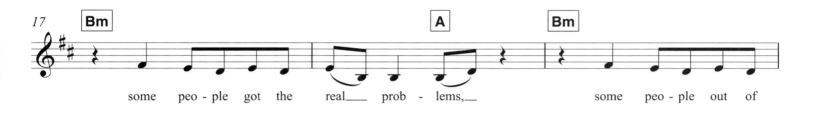

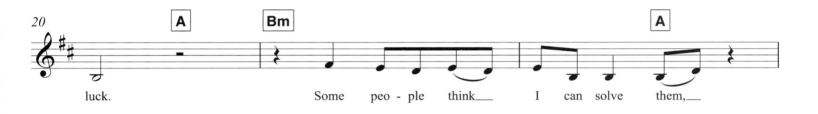

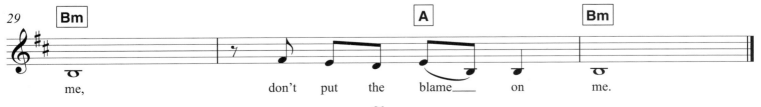

I Would Like

Words & Music by Zara Larsson, Oliver Peterhof, Marcus Lomax, Jordan Johnson, Alexander Izquierdo, Anthony Kelly, Karen Chin, James Abrahart & Stefan Johnson

Larsson brings back the 1990s in this adaptation of Sasha's 1998 tune 'Dat Sexy Body'. Sasha's original version harks back to her Jamaican roots, with elements of reggae and dancehall, while Larsson reinvents the song as a millennial club classic. In one performance of 'I Would Like', Larsson made headlines for an entirely different reason—a bizarre choice of stage outfit saw her wearing a bright pink, fluffy coat, leading the press to make comparisons with the British children's TV character Bagpuss!

Hints & Tips: This piece is simpler than it might look—there's lots of repetition in the melody.

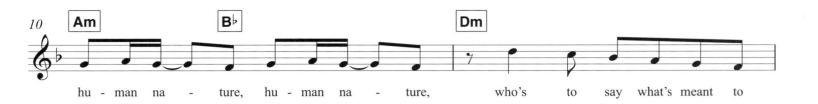

hu - man na - ture, hu - man na - ture, who's to say what's meant to

be?_____ Oh, why can't we be on our

worst be - hav - iour, worst be - hav - iour, when it comes so nat - 'ral -

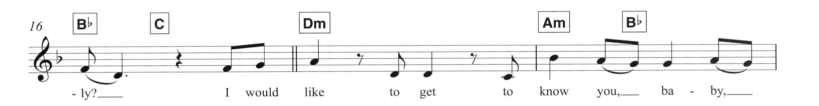

- ly?_____ I would like to get to know you,___ ba - by,___

like to get un - der your sex - y bo - dy. I would

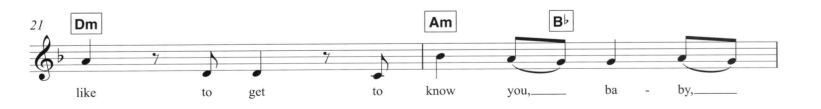

like to get to know you,_____ ba - by,_____

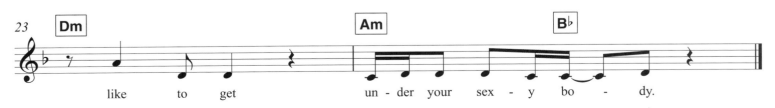

like to get un - der your sex - y bo - dy.

Let Me Love You

Words & Music by Justin Bieber, William Grigahcine, Brian Lee, Steven Marsden,
Andrew Wotman, Carl Rosen, Teddy Mendez & Edwin Perez
Arranged by Alex Tamposi, Louis Bell & Lumidee Cedeno

From his debut album, *Encore*, DJ Snake collaborated with young pop idol Justin Bieber for this track about a guy who refuses to give up on his relationship. The album cover art shows DJ Snake in the desert, walking towards a French metro station, which illustrates his dual heritage—his parents are from North Africa and he himself is Parisian. The DJ is well known for his dancefloor anthems, having had previous hits like 'Turn Down For What', featuring rapper Lil Jon.

Hints & Tips: Divide the crotchet beats into four semiquavers in your mind to ensure you place the dotted rhythms precisely, particularly in bars 3 and 7.

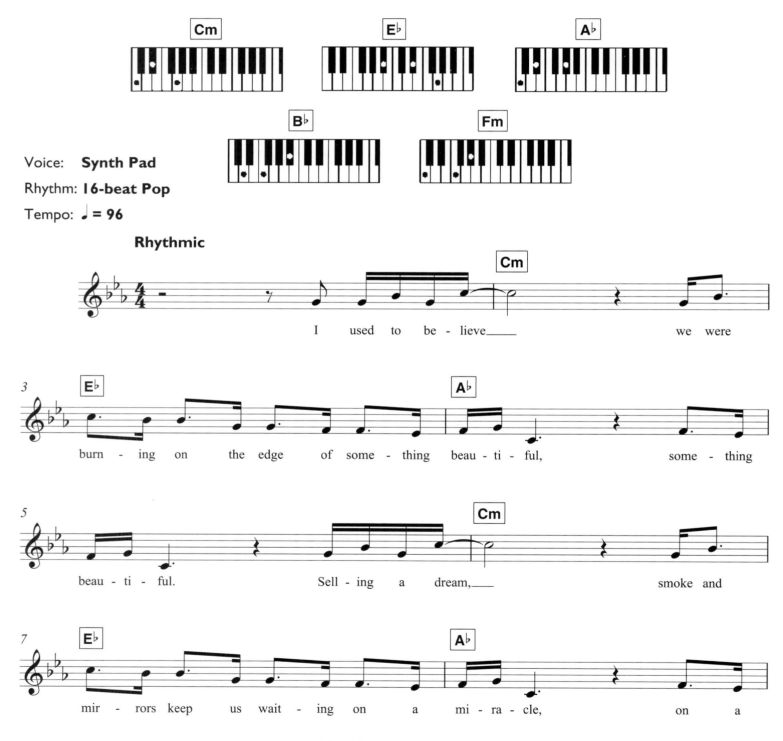

Voice: **Synth Pad**

Rhythm: **16-beat Pop**

Tempo: ♩ = 96

mi - ra - cle.   Say,   go through the   dark - est   of   days,

hea - ven's a   heart - break   a - way.   Nev - er   let you go,   nev - er   let me   down.__

_____   Oh,   it's been a   hell of a ride,   driv - ing the edge of a knife.

Nev - er   let you go,   nev - er   let me down._____   Don't you give up,__

___ na,___ na, na.   I won't give up,___ na,___ na, na. Let me   love   you,   let me

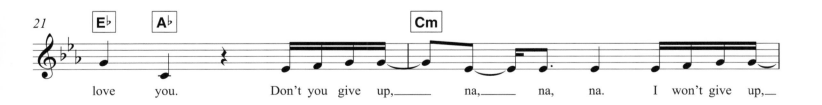

love   you.   Don't you give   up,_____   na,_____ na,   na.   I won't give up,__

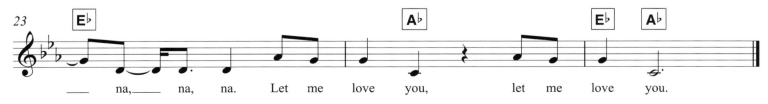

___ na,___ na, na.   Let me   love   you,   let me   love   you.

No Lie

Words & Music by Sean Henriques, Jamie Sanderson, Philip Kembo, Emily Schwartz & Andrew Jackson

Sean Paul brought dancehall to the masses in 2002 with 'Gimme The Light', the first single from his debut album, *Dutty Rock*. Since then, he has continued to dominate the urban charts with hit after hit. He wrote 'No Lie' with two songwriters, one of whom was a friend of the singer Dua Lipa. The song was played to her and she loved it, so plans were made for Lipa to sing on the track with Sean Paul.

Hints & Tips: Bring out the contrast between the light, detached, repeated semiquavers and the smooth, slurred, descending quavers from bar 9 onwards to imitate the duetting parts.

Voice: **Steel Pans**

Rhythm: **Cuban Pop**

Tempo: ♩ = 96

Jaunty

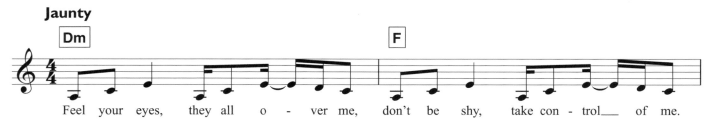

Feel your eyes, they all o - ver me, don't be shy, take con - trol___ of me.

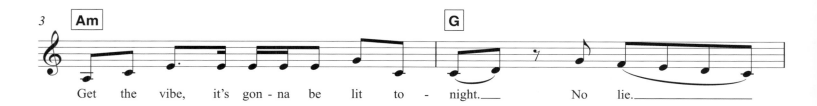

Get the vibe, it's gon - na be lit to - night.___ No lie.___

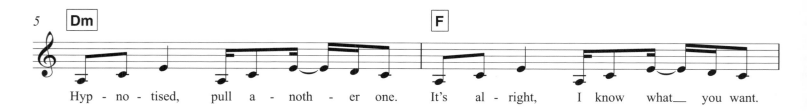

Hyp - no - tised, pull a - noth - er one. It's al - right, I know what___ you want.

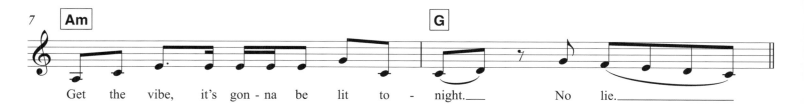

Get the vibe, it's gon - na be lit to - night.___ No lie.___

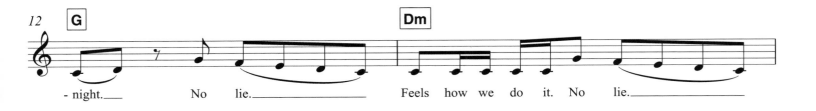

Not In Love

Words & Music by Fred Gibson, Edvard Erfjord,
Henrik Michelsen, Rachel Keen & James Bell

The all-girl trio M.O formed back in 2012 and generated public interest later that year when they performed a remixed cover of Brandy & Monica's 'The Boy Is Mine' with rapper Lady Leshurr. Since then, they've become known for their 1990s throwback style in both fashion and music, leaving fans hoping for a debut album release in the near future.

Hints & Tips: The triplet quavers in bars 8–9 and 13–14 should be of equal length. Clap the rhythm before you play it.

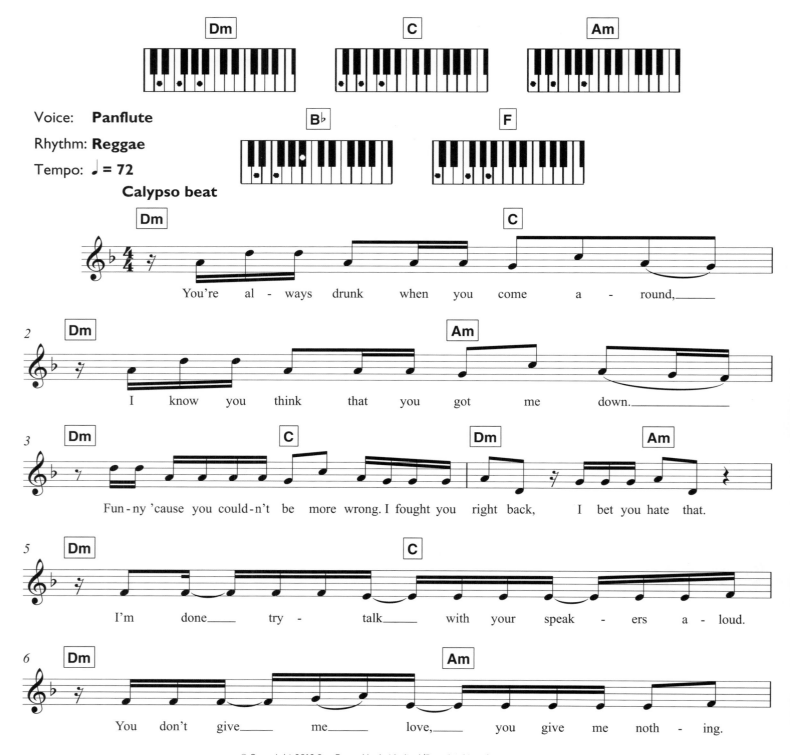

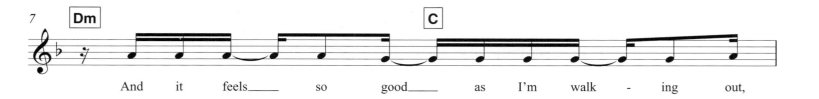

And it feels___ so good___ as I'm walk - ing out,

out of your house_ and I'm scream-ing, 'I'm not___ in love,_____ I'm not___ in

love no more.'_ I wan-na shout it and tell the world, I - I - I love it,

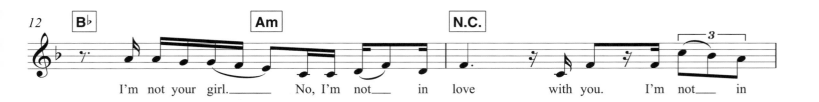

I'm not your girl._____ No, I'm not___ in love with you. I'm not___ in

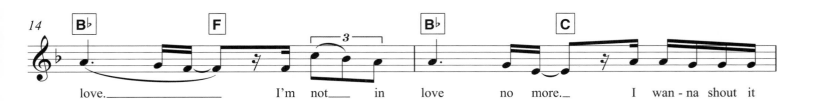

love._____ I'm not___ in love no more._ I wan-na shout it

and tell the world, I - I - I love it, I'm not your girl._____ No, I'm not___ in

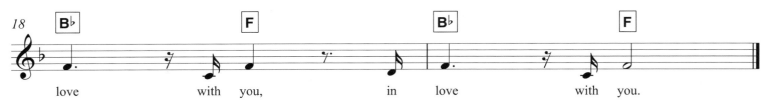

love with you, in love with you.

Now And Later

**Words & Music by Ian Kirkpatrick, Andreas Schuller, Joe Spargur,
Dominic Woods, James Wong & Leroy Clampitt**

'Now And Later', from Sage The Gemini's album, *Bachelor Party*, was named after the American sweet of the same name.
Now and Laters come in 19 flavours, but in the song, Sage The Gemini implies there are '31 flavours', believed to be
a nod to his notion to write music that can 'please everybody' and access as many listeners as possible. In an
interview, the artist revealed that he lost a wobbly tooth to one of the sweets when he was younger!

Hints & Tips: There are a few syncopated rhythms in this song — clap through the piece before you play.

We Don't Talk Anymore

Words & Music by Jacob Hindlin, Charlie Puth & Selena Gomez

Charlie Puth wrote this song after chatting to a friend who had been infatuated with a girl for months previously, but in a follow-up conversation, had said to him, 'we don't talk anymore'. In an attempt to lighten the mood, Puth started singing the phrase back to him, which resulted in the conception of the song. Selena Gomez agreed to feature on this track as she had experienced an on-off relationship in the public eye and felt she had a personal connection with the lyrics.

Hints & Tips: Take a minute to read through the lyrics of this song in time to ensure that you follow the written rhythm exactly. Try tapping your hand on your knee to keep a steady crotchet pulse as you do so.

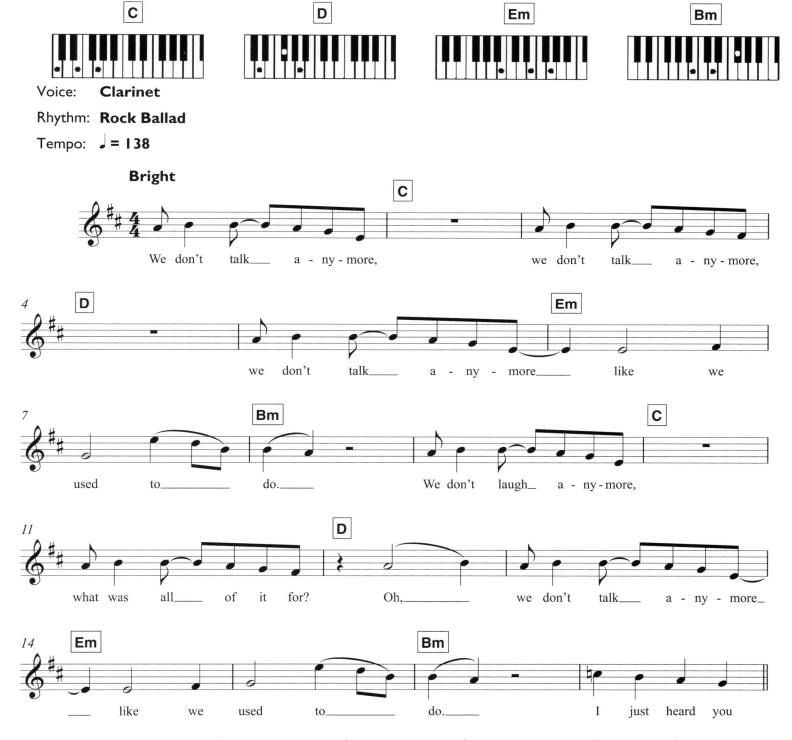

On Hold

Words & Music by Daryl Hall, Sara Allen, John Oates, James Smith, Romy Madley Croft & Oliver Sim

Five years since their previous album, *Coexist*, The xx released *I See You* in 2017, with 'On Hold' as their first single. The band is known for their understated, electropop style, which is evident in this track, along with their distinctive alternate male and female vocal lines. However, the *I See You* album shows The xx taking their style in a more playful direction, saying that the five-year hiatus was hugely beneficial for their musical growth.

Hints & Tips: Before you begin, practise the right-hand part in bars 10–12 until you are comfortable switching between crotchet triplets and regular crotchets and quavers.

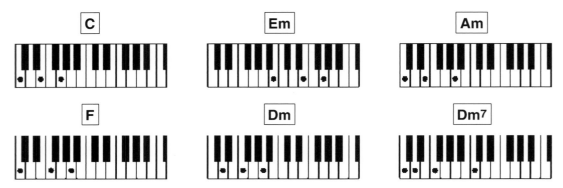

Voice: **Electric Organ**

Rhythm: **Soul Ballad**

Tempo: = 124

Wistful

Rockabye

Words & Music by Steve McCutcheon, Sean Henriques,
Ina Wroldsen, Ammar Malik & Jack Patterson

After their storming 2014 No. 1 hit, 'Rather Be', Clean Bandit released 'Rockabye' two years later to similarly raving reviews and another No. 1 spot. It was the first song released by the band after the departure of violinist Neil Milan, who was responsible for co-creating the group. The track features dancehall superstar Sean Paul and contemporary English singer-songwriter Anne-Marie.

Hints & Tips: Play this melody in a light, detached manner to emulate the jaunty, summery vibe of the original record.

12 my love,___ no - bo - dy mat - ters like you.'_____ She tells him,

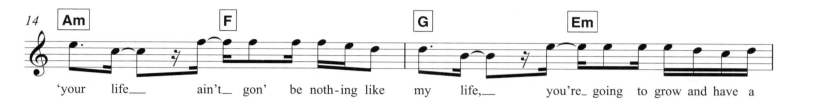

14 'your life___ ain't___ gon' be noth-ing like my life,___ you're_ going to grow and have a

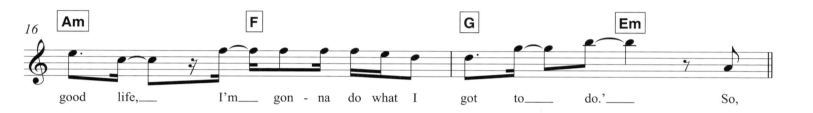

16 good life,___ I'm___ gon - na do what I got to___ do.'___ So,

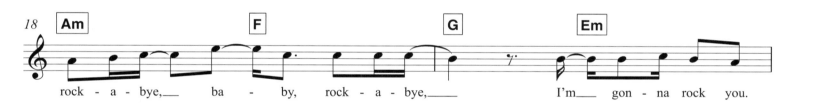

18 rock - a - bye,___ ba - by, rock - a - bye,___ I'm___ gon - na rock you.

20 Rock - a - bye,___ ba - by, don't you cry,___ some - bo - dy's got you.

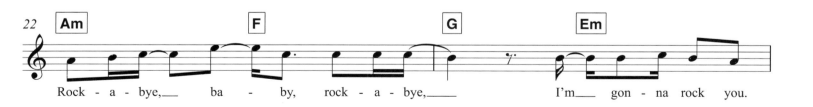

22 Rock - a - bye,___ ba - by, rock - a - bye,___ I'm___ gon - na rock you.

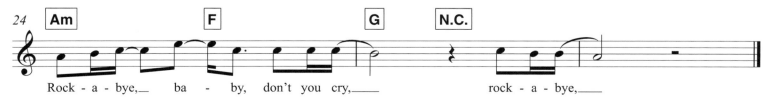

24 Rock - a - bye,___ ba - by, don't you cry,___ rock - a - bye,___

September Song

Words & Music by Benjamin McIldowie, Teemu Brunila, Jon Hume & John Paul Cooper

The Manchester-born singer-songwriter JP Cooper had been making waves in the underground music scene for a few years before he reached No. 1 in the UK Official Singles Chart when he appeared on Jonas Blue's track 'Perfect Strangers' in 2016. He was still relatively new to chart success when 'September Song' was released. The song describes a guy's feelings about a girl with whom he had a short-lived teenage romance.

Hints & Tips: Practise switching between regular quavers and triplet quavers by speaking through the lyrics in rhythm before you play.

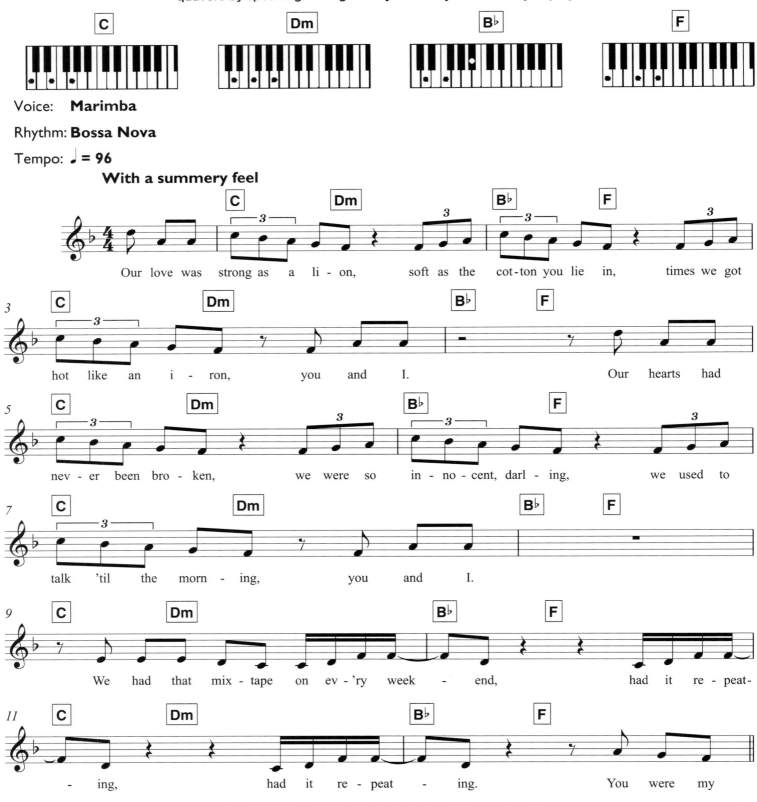

Voice: **Marimba**

Rhythm: **Bossa Nova**

Tempo: ♩ = 96

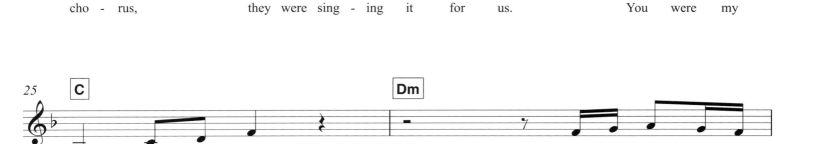

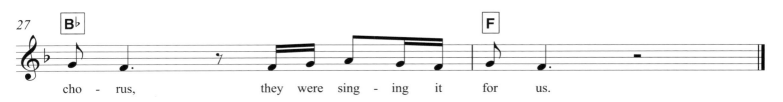

Shape Of You

Words & Music by Steve Mac, Ed Sheeran & John McDaid

Ed Sheeran co-wrote this track with Snow Patrol's Johnny McDaid and producer Steve Mac. He released this and 'Castle On The Hill' simultaneously, scoring him both the No. 1 and No. 2 spots in the charts in record-breaking fashion!

Hints & Tips: This piece has lots of repeated semiquavers. They will require a loose wrist and a light touch to help you float along through the melody.

Voice: **Flute**

Rhythm: **Samba**

Tempo: ♩ = 82

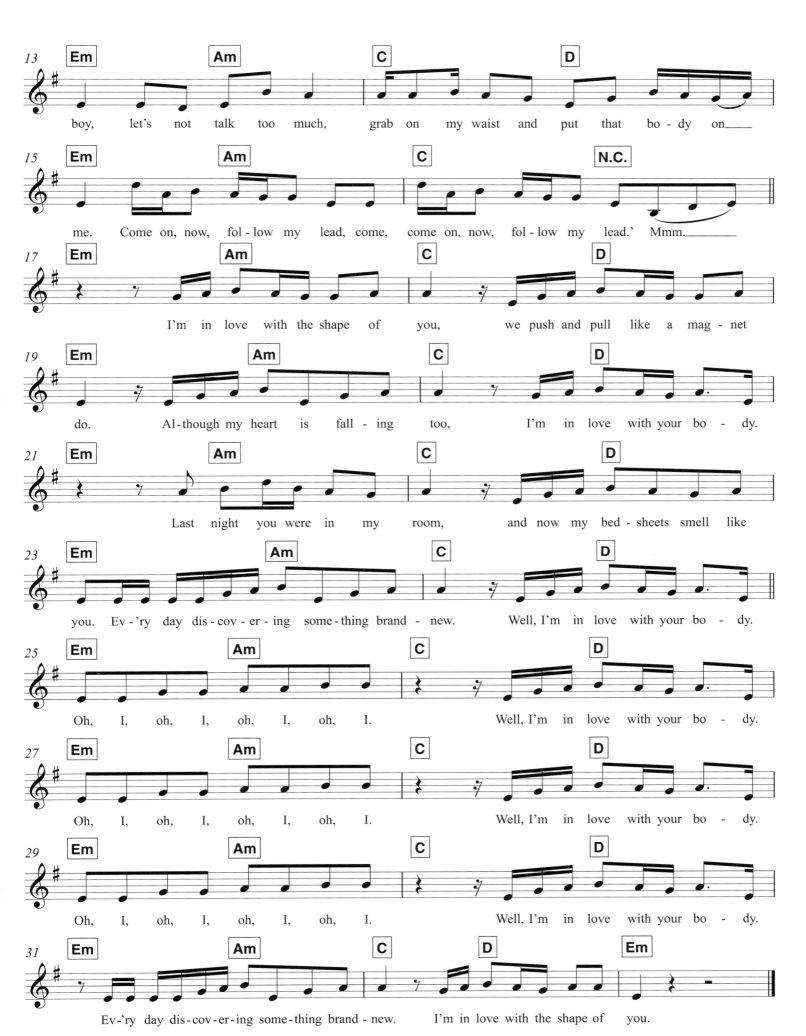

So Good

Words & Music by Steve Mac, Edward Drewett & Chelcee Grimes

This is the debut single from X Factor winner Louisa Johnson, who took the 12th UK series by storm back in 2015 and became the programme's youngest winner to date. Before releasing 'So Good', Johnson had already warmed up the crowd by working with electronic pop band Clean Bandit on their track, 'Tears', in 2016.

Hints & Tips: Contrast a mysterious verse with a powerful chorus by using your full arm weight and strong fingers to create a louder dynamic and fuller sound from the middle of bar 12.

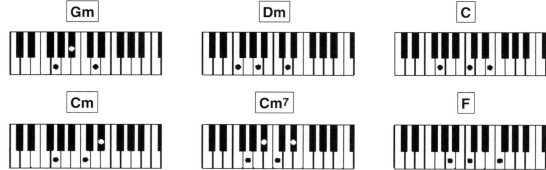

Voice: **Cello**

Rhythm: **Rock Ballad**

Tempo: ♩ = 70

Steady

I said I'm 'bout five min-utes a-way,___ one more stop and I'll be off this train.___

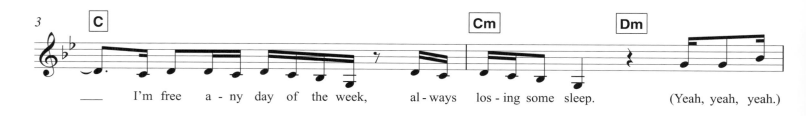

___ I'm free a-ny day of the week, al-ways los-ing some sleep. (Yeah, yeah, yeah.)

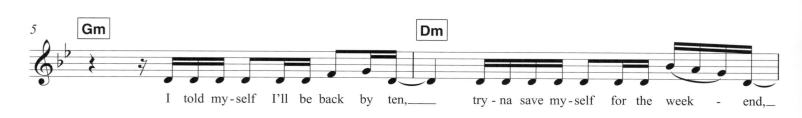

I told my-self I'll be back by ten,___ try-na save my-self for the week - end,___

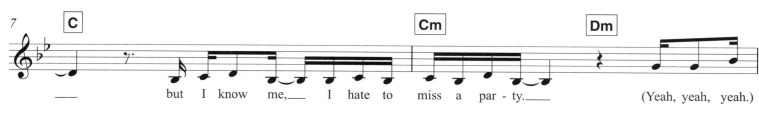

___ but I know me,___ I hate to miss a par-ty.___ (Yeah, yeah, yeah.)

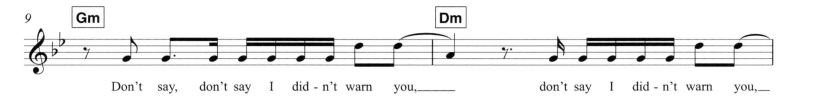
Don't say, don't say I did-n't warn you,_____ don't say I did-n't warn you,__

__ I live for the mo - ment. I was-n't sup-posed to go

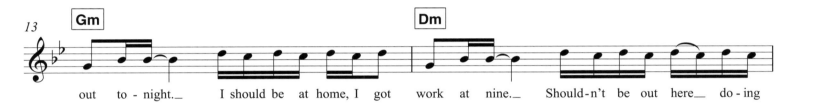
out to - night.__ I should be at home, I got work at nine.__ Should-n't be out here__ do-ing

what I like,__ but it feels so good, so good. I was on-ly gon-na be an

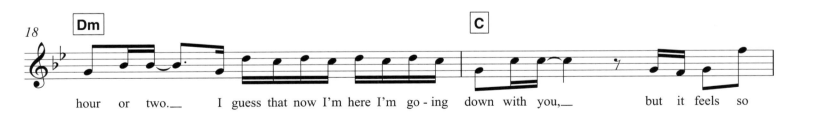
hour or two.__ I guess that now I'm here I'm go - ing down with you,__ but it feels so

good, so good, so_____ good._____

Starboy

**Words & Music by Thomas Bangalter, Guy-Manuel de Homem-Christo,
Henry Russell Walter, Jason Quenneville, Abel Tesfaye & Martin McKinney**

This track's title was inspired by David Bowie's 'Starman', but this is where the similarities between the two songs end.
While Bowie focuses on the other-worldliness of a potential 'Starman', it is believed that 'Starboy' is an introduction
to The Weeknd's new alter ego, having chopped off his famous dreadlocks and used the song's music video
to debut his new look. The tune is the title track of his 2016 album of the same name.

**Hints & Tips: Make sure you keep the second semiquaver on the word 'ah' short to mimic the
vocal inflection on the track. Be careful not to rush the semiquavers from bar 9 onwards.**

Voice: **Space Pad**

Rhythm: **House**

Tempo: ♩ = 82

Precisely

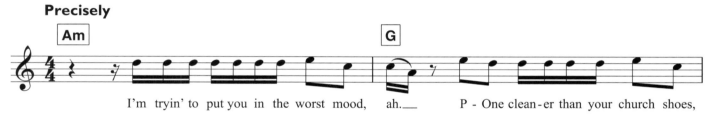

I'm tryin' to put you in the worst mood, ah.___ P - One clean-er than your church shoes,

ah.___ Mil - li point two, just to hurt you, ah.___ All red Lamb' just to tease you,

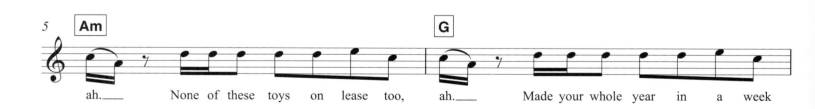

ah.___ None of these toys on lease too, ah.___ Made your whole year in a week

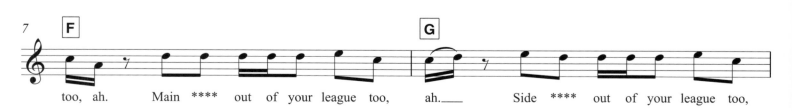

too, ah. Main **** out of your league too, ah.___ Side **** out of your league too,

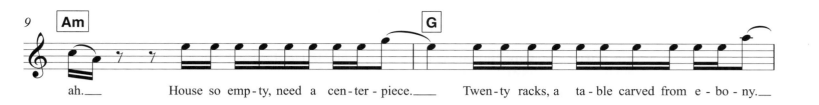

ah.___ House so emp-ty, need a cen-ter-piece.___ Twen-ty racks, a ta-ble carved from e-bo-ny.___

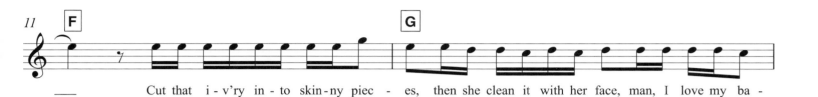

___ Cut that i-v'ry in-to skin-ny piec - es, then she clean it with her face, man, I love my ba -

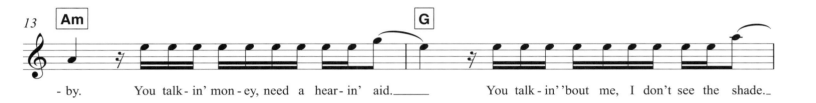

- by. You talk-in' mon-ey, need a hear-in' aid.___ You talk-in' 'bout me, I don't see the shade.___

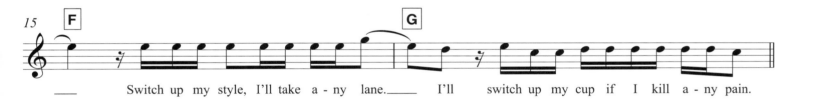

___ Switch up my style, I'll take a-ny lane.___ I'll switch up my cup if I kill a-ny pain.

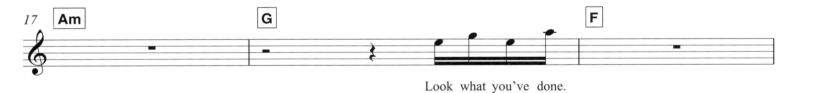

Look what you've done.

I'm a mo'-****-in' star-boy.___ Look what you've done.

I'm a mo'-****-in' star-boy.___

You Don't Know Me

Words & Music by Uzoechi Emenike, Timucin Aluo, Janee Bennett, Rachel Keen, Phil D Young, Peter Hayo, Walter Merziger, Arno Kammermeier & DJ Pat Bo

For Jax Jones, settling on the perfect bass line was the most difficult part of writing 'You Don't Know Me'. Having been obsessed with M.A.N.D.Y vs Booka Shade's 2005 track, 'Body Language', for so long, he decided to try out their bassline with his own song and realised it was a match! Jones said that the combination was a perfect way of bringing 'classic techno to our new house setting'.

Hints & Tips: In preparation for playing a piece in this key, practise some chromatic scales to get used to crossing your index finger over your thumb.

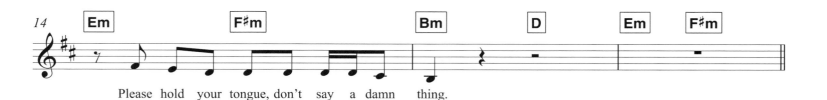

Please hold your tongue, don't say a damn thing.

See your i-Phone cam-er-a flash-in'. Please step back, it's my__ style you're cramp-in'.

You here for long? 'Oh, no,__ I'm just pass-in'.' Do you want a drink? 'No,__ thanks for ask-in'.'

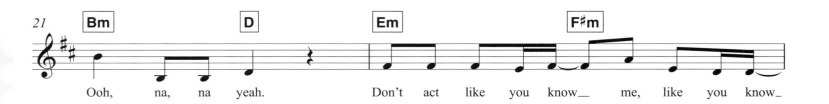

Ooh, na, na yeah. Don't act like you know__ me, like you know__

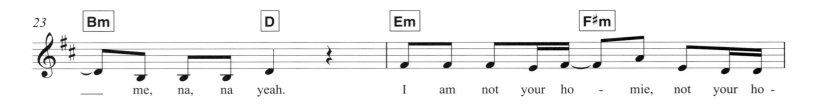

__ me, na, na yeah. I am not your ho-mie, not your ho-

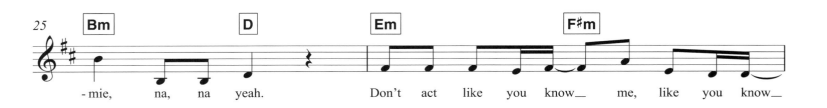

- mie, na, na yeah. Don't act like you know__ me, like you know__

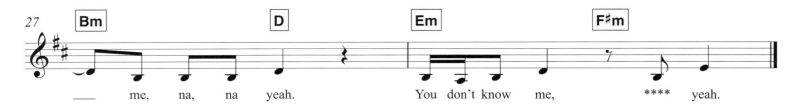

__ me, na, na yeah. You don't know me, **** yeah.

You Want Me

Words & Music by Luke Reid, Corey Johnson, Thomas Courtney & Darren Martyn

Tom Zanetti released this dance-house track, which became his first single to reach the charts, with Sadia Ama, the little sister of 'You Might Need Somebody' singer, Shola Ama. The Leeds-born entrepreneur describes himself as a 'man of all trades'—together with his music career as a DJ, producer, rapper and songwriter, Zanetti also clocks in ownership of four festivals as well as several overseas businesses and is looking to set up a barbershop and a clothing brand in the near future!

Hints & Tips: Practise this melody with a metronome or drum beat accompaniment to ensure you aren't tempted to rush the quavers; keep the simple rhythms steady.

Voice: **Synth Chorus**

Rhythm: **Dance Beat**

Tempo: ♩ = 124

Mysterious

Ba - by, I'm not here to start a fight but I

just thought I'd let you know. 'Cause the way that you've been

treat - ing me, is so un - fair, ba - by, it's so cold.

You want me, you want me,

you want me, a - ny - time you want me.

You want me, you want me, you want me,

a - ny - time you want me too.